Sandy's Song

by Barbara Brooks Simons

illustrated by Annabel Kendall

Table of Contents

Chapter 1
The Prize. 2

Chapter 2
Anticipation! 7

Chapter 3
An Impossible Dream?. 10

Chapter 4
On Stage!. 16

Comprehension Check 20

Chapter 1

The Prize

Alexandra's fingers flew over the keyboard of the grand piano. The audience watched in silence as she made her way through the difficult passages and beautiful melodies of a piano sonata by Franz Schubert. This afternoon was a special occasion for Alexandra and all the other students at the Metropolitan Music School. Their annual spring recital was a chance to show off the hard work and practice that they had put in during the winter.

Alexandra's chestnut brown hair was in a neat bun like a ballerina's, tied with a velvet ribbon—not her usual bouncy ponytail. Her long, blue velvet skirt fell gracefully to the floor around the piano bench. She reached the end of the piece and sat back. The people in the audience broke into applause.

"So talented for a teenager," one woman whispered to her neighbor. "Isn't it a shame about. . . ." But her neighbor couldn't hear the rest of the sentence because the applause drowned it out.

Still sitting on the bench, the young pianist turned toward the audience. "My next piece is one of my favorites, a short, two-part invention by J.S. Bach," Alexandra said.

Again, she played beautifully, and the applause was loud and enthusiastic. Waiting offstage in the wings, Alexandra's parents smiled proudly.

Her teacher, Mrs. Meier, looked pleased and happy, too. "I have a little surprise for all of you," Mrs. Meier whispered to Alexandra's parents, "but it has to wait until all the others have played."

People were still applauding, although Alexandra's part of the program was over. She reached down to the floor and picked up the crutches that had been lying out of sight of the audience. Then she stood up a little awkwardly and, using the crutches, slowly left the stage. The long, blue velvet skirt still hid the heavy leg braces Alexandra wore.

Some people in the audience were surprised, but their applause grew even louder. The woman who had spoken earlier turned to her neighbor again. "As I said before, Sandy is such a talented pianist. But she had polio when she was a small child. I heard that she got sick a year before they brought out the vaccine in 1955. It left her legs paralyzed."

As the student recital continued, Alexandra's best friend, Elena, played a slow, lovely solo on her cello. Their good friend Ben was next. Ben was 16. He had come to the school as a boy soprano, but his voice had changed and deepened, so now it was a rich, mellow baritone. More of their fellow students played and sang. When the recital ended, all the students appeared on stage, and the audience applauded them all over again.

Then Mrs. Meier stepped out from between the curtains. She was a tall woman in a long gown, with her hair in a bun much like the one Alexandra was wearing. She held up her hand for silence.

"Hasn't this been a wonderful evening?" she asked. Everyone applauded again. She went on, "As I'm sure you heard this evening, all of these marvelously talented students have made wonderful progress this year. But every year we also give a prize for one student who's been outstanding. I'm sure you won't be surprised that this year's winner is Alexandra Parker, whom some of you know as Sandy."

Now the applause got even louder. Mrs. Meier smiled as she tried to quiet the crowd. "Don't you want to know what the prize is? I'm sure you've all heard of the wonderful young concert pianist Frederick Lin? And have you tried to get tickets to his concert?"

There were "oohs" from some people in the audience. Others chuckled, because the concert had been sold out for months.

"So here's Sandy's prize: a trip to the city by limousine, with dinner at a very fine restaurant, and then," she paused, "tickets to the Frederick Lin concert—the best seats in the house. Plus, she'll have a chance to meet with Frederick Lin backstage. But Sandy doesn't have to go alone. She can choose two friends to share both the dinner and the special box seats for the concert."

Sandy could hardly believe her ears. She moved forward on her crutches, smiling happily as Mrs. Meier hugged her. Sandy took the envelope of tickets and went offstage, where her parents were waiting. She looked toward the back row just a minute to wink at her two best friends. Ben and Elena exchanged glances and grins.

Chapter 2

Anticipation!

It was lunchtime at the music school. In one of the rehearsal rooms, Sandy and her girlfriends were eating lunch and talking about the concert. All of them would have loved to have won the prize. But Sandy was popular as well as talented, and no one begrudged her this special evening. Other students understood that every day brought challenges for Sandy. Whether she was using her crutches or her wheelchair, Sandy often faced obstacles.

Everyone also assumed that Elena and Ben would share the evening with Sandy. The three friends had been close since two years earlier. Then they had all been newcomers to the school, wondering whether they really had the musical talent they needed to succeed. Sandy had had to get special permission because she was six months younger than the required age for admission.

Sandy was perched on the piano bench. Her wheelchair was parked nearby. As she fiddled around with popular songs, her hands danced on the keyboard. She began with "I Want to Hold Your Hand." Sandy shifted from the Beatles to the Beach Boys and then to the ballad "Blue Velvet." The song had been one of the top 10 songs of the year before.

"Frederick Lin sometimes plays popular music too, doesn't he?" Joanie asked.

"He does, and sometimes he arranges it so it sounds like classical music, which is fun. Listen to this—it's how 'Blue Velvet' would sound if you played it in the style of Mozart." The other music students laughed as Sandy played a rippling melody. "But that's not really what I want to hear him play. I'm hoping for a lot of Chopin— the waltzes and etudes, especially. He plays them so beautifully."

"Speaking of blue velvet, what are you going to wear?" Joanie asked. That was something everyone wanted to know.

"Oh, it has to be the blue velvet skirt again," Sandy said. "It's the dressiest and most grown-up thing I own. I've never been to that concert hall before. And we have box seats, so I'd like to look kind of elegant!"

The bell rang, and lunch was over. Sandy pulled the wheelchair over to the piano bench and settled herself into it. She put her crutches on her lap and then wheeled into the corridor on her way to her next class.

Then, finally, it was the night before the concert. Sandy tried to do her homework, but it was hard to concentrate on math. Her mother brought in a cup of scalding hot cocoa. While waiting for it to cool, Sandy put on a record of Frederick Lin playing the piano.

"I really hope I can play like that someday," she told her mother. "The restaurant and the great seats for the concert will be wonderful. The chance to meet Frederick Lin and get his autograph will be even better. But just hearing him play like that will be the best thing of all."

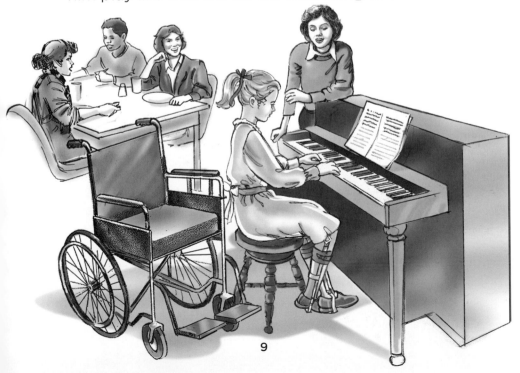

Chapter 3

An Impossible Dream?

As they waited for the limousine on the night of the concert, Sandy, Elena, and Ben looked at each other and laughed. They looked so different from the way they did at school. "Don't we look elegant!" Sandy said. "You'd think we rode in limousines every day." They were almost too excited to sit still in the back seat as the long black limousine sped downtown. "I feel like a movie star," sighed Elena.

"Don't get used to it," Ben warned. "On Monday it's back to paying your fare on the bus."

"I do feel a little like Cinderella," Sandy sighed. "I wonder if this limousine turns into a pumpkin at midnight?"

The limousine pulled up to the door of the restaurant. The driver unloaded Sandy's wheelchair and took it inside to the cloakroom. They had decided to bring the chair since it might be the easiest way for Sandy to get from the restaurant to the concert hall.

Ben helped Sandy out of the limousine and handed her the crutches. They started across the sidewalk to the restaurant door. Then they stopped and looked at the five steps leading up to the double doors of the restaurant. Ben looked worried for a minute.

"No, it'll be okay," Sandy said. "I can manage that many steps." They got up the stairs and through the door into the restaurant. Wonderful smells surrounded them. The uneasy moment was over.

The manager greeted them and helped Sandy to their table. Dinner was excellent, and the waiters made sure the three friends had everything they wanted.

Soon it was time to leave for the concert. It was early, and the concert hall was only a few blocks away, but they agreed that the wheelchair would be the best way to go. Along the way, Sandy's friends teased her. "Oh, Madame Alexandra, thank you for being such a great pianist and winning this great evening," Ben said.

"Next year, it's your turn, Maestro, with your golden voice," Sandy joked back. They turned the corner to get to the front entrance of the concert hall. Then they stopped and stared. "Oh, no," Elena wailed. Sandy was too stunned to say anything. "Philharmonia Hall" was chiseled in the granite block above the doors—but three long flights of steps led up to the entrance.

What were they going to do? "I can't possibly climb that many stairs with my crutches," Sandy said very softly. Her voice broke slightly as she tried not to cry. There was no way they could get the wheelchair up the steps.

The three friends stood at the bottom of the steps, looking up. The three flights might as well have been a mile high. Other concertgoers streamed past them. Some looked curiously at the group at the bottom of the stairs. Sandy could see her dream evening vanishing like a burst balloon. She clenched her fingers tightly around the arm of the chair.

Suddenly they heard excited voices. They turned to see a young man getting out of a limousine that was parked at the curb. It was Frederick Lin himself.

He approached and bowed to Sandy. "You must be Alexandra Parker, our special guest," he said. "Mrs. Meier tells me you're a fine pianist. She was my teacher once, too, you know."

Sandy was too upset and angry to be polite, even though her hero was standing right in front of her. She blurted out: "Yes, that's me, but they didn't say how really special I am, did they? No one thought about my crutches or wheelchair, did they? I don't know how I'll ever get in to hear you play. What am I supposed to do—crawl up the steps?

"Why isn't there another entrance? And an elevator? I'm not the only one who needs help. Don't people like me have any rights? I probably can't even get to those fancy box seats we're supposed to sit in."

A worried look spread over Lin's pleasant face. He leaned down to talk to Sandy. "Hey, I'm really sorry. Mrs. Meier did tell me you used crutches, but neither of us thought to worry about these stairs. People don't think, I guess, not unless they're in the same fix."

Then suddenly Lin smiled. "No, wait," he said. "We can fix this. In fact, there is an elevator, around by the stage door. The musicians and stagehands use it."

"And as for getting to the box seats, you're right. The way the hall is built, you probably would have trouble with your chair."

Lin turned to Ben and Elena. "You two use those box seats. They're excellent, but I'll make sure that your friend gets to sit somewhere even better. That's a promise."

Chapter 4

On Stage!

It was almost time for the concert to begin. Elena and Ben settled back in their plush red seats. They looked over the carved edge of the box at the well-dressed audience in the concert hall. The red and gold decorations in the old-fashioned hall were spectacular.

"These seats are wonderful," Elena exclaimed. "Sandy was right, though. Even if she could get up the steps, I don't think these seats would have been comfortable for her—and certainly her chair wouldn't have fit."

"She was right to get angry, too," Ben added. "It's not fair—and people just don't realize. We're her best friends, and we know there are things she can't do, but I didn't think it would be hard for Sandy to get into the concert!"

Elena agreed. "There ought to be ramps or elevators or something in public buildings like these. People who can't walk or are in wheelchairs have rights, just like everybody else. They need to be able to get to work and go to movies and concerts and restaurants."

"I just realized," Ben said, "that the only reason Sandy gets around pretty well at school is kind of an accident. Since the school used to be an office building, it has elevators and nice, straight corridors. And the lobby is level with the sidewalk. It doesn't have steps like the restaurant had. Sandy probably wouldn't fare so well at another school." He looked at his watch. "It's almost time for the concert to start."

Elena looked around the theater again. "I sure hope Frederick Lin really is looking after Sandy. He seemed like a nice guy."

"I really wonder where she is, though." Ben sounded worried. "I don't see anyone in a wheelchair down on the main floor. Besides, he promised to give Sandy a special seat, and those aren't as good as these."

Just then, the lights in the concert hall dimmed. The hum of conversation from the audience stopped. The gold curtains drew back to reveal a grand piano in the center of the stage. On either side of the stage were three rows of chairs where Frederick Lin's special guests were sitting. Elena and Ben recognized several of them as famous musicians. The others must have been Lin's family and friends. All the women in the stage seats wore elegant gowns, while the men wore dark suits or tuxedos.

At the end of the first row sat Sandy in her wheelchair, looking proud and happy. Elena was so thrilled that she bounced up and down in her plush box seat. "Oh, look, look," she whispered to Ben. Elena leaned over the edge and waved, although she knew Sandy probably couldn't see her.

Frederick Lin walked on stage, and the audience applauded loudly. He bowed toward them and then toward everyone on stage. Then he sat down and began to play. From their box, Ben and Elena could see his hands moving rapidly over the black and white keys. From time to time, they looked at each other and nodded approval. Lin was just as brilliant as Ben and Elena had expected him to be.

Sandy was in another world— one that was almost perfect. In the pure joy of being there, she almost forgot the hurt she had felt earlier that evening. Each piece that Lin played seemed more wonderful than the one before. There were the Chopin etudes she had hoped for. There was Schubert, who she already loved.

Finally, Lin finished his regular program, and applause thundered through the hall. The young pianist turned to the audience. "I have a special guest tonight, who's a pretty good pianist herself. I won't embarrass her by pointing her out, but this encore is for her. It's a little piece I wrote myself. I call it 'Sandy's Song.'"

Comprehension Check

Summarize

Use a Character, Setting Chart to help you retell *Sandy's Song*. Why does Sandy win tickets to a concert? What threatens to prevent her from enjoying her reward? How is Sandy's problem solved?

Character	Setting

Think and Compare

1. Look back at pages 14–15. Summarize what Sandy says about the barriers that prevent people with disabilities from getting into many buildings. What solutions does she suggest? *(Analyze Character and Setting)*

2. Think about a time when you felt treated unfairly, as Sandy does at the concert hall. How did you react? What happened afterward? *(Synthesize)*

3. From your own observations of public buildings and other spaces, do you think experiences like Sandy's had an effect on how buildings are designed and built today? Explain your answer. *(Evaluate)*